Pim the imp is naughty, too.
Loves to hide your sock or shoe.
See him now. He's proudly bobbin',
Wearing scarlet, like a robin!

Hob the goblin likes to play
Cheeky tricks, the livelong day.
But he *will* behave tonight,
In his party suit of white.

Dizzy is the wizard wise.
Magic makes, before your eyes.
Lo! He waves his wand, and see!
Clad in shining gold is he!

Winnie Witch, from Dingly Dell,
(Careful, she might cast a spell)
Puts a star on her tall hat,
Ribbons round her pussy cat.

Now turn to the back of the book and see where the fairy folk are going.

£2.20

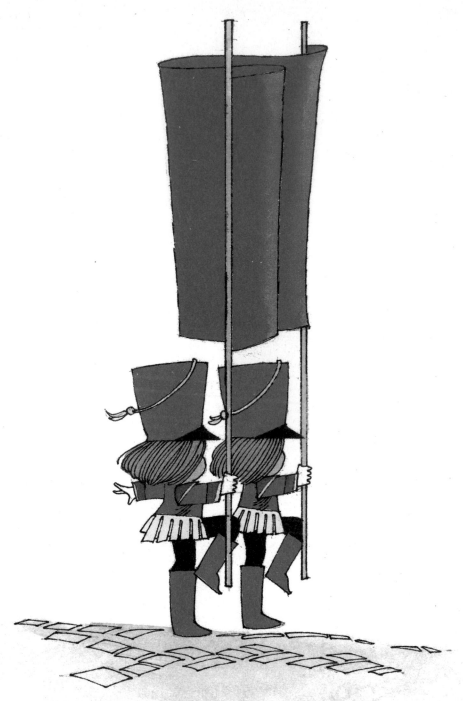

Printed and Published by D. C. Thomson & Co., Ltd., Dundee and London.

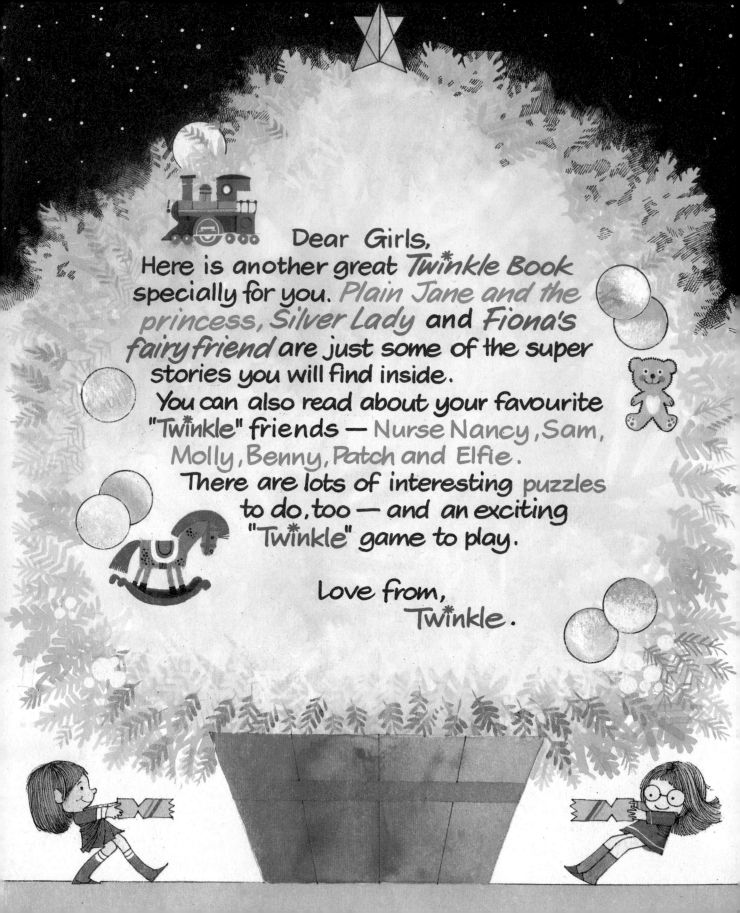

Dear Girls,

Here is another great *Twinkle Book* specially for you. *Plain Jane and the princess, Silver Lady* and *Fiona's fairy friend* are just some of the super stories you will find inside.

You can also read about your favourite "Twinkle" friends — Nurse Nancy, Sam, Molly, Benny, Patch and Elfie.

There are lots of interesting puzzles to do, too — and an exciting "Twinkle" game to play.

Love from,
Twinkle.

Nancy the little nurse

1 — Nancy, the little nurse, was going shopping with her young brother, John. As they passed the theatre, John saw a pantomime poster. "Oh, look!" he cried.

2 — "This year's pantomime is 'Mother Goose'! I'd love to see it," added John. "I'm afraid we can't go," said Nancy. "The tickets are too dear for us."

3 — Later, when Nancy arrived at the Dollies Hospital, she was amazed to see a large golden egg on the floor! "Who does *that* belong to?" she gasped.

4 — Suddenly, Nancy saw a goose walking through the ward! "I must be seeing things!" cried Nancy. Then she heard the goose laughing. "It's a goose costume," said Nancy.

5 — Just then, Colin, the ambulance boy, opened the costume and popped his head out. "Hello!" he laughed. "I hope I didn't give you a fright."

6 — Nancy's grandad explained that the costume and the egg were from the "Mother Goose" pantomime. "The theatre asked us to mend them," he said.

7 — Nancy began to work on the cracked egg. "I'll give it a fresh coat of gold paint and make it look as good as new for the show," she smiled.

8 — That afternoon, two of the theatre crew came and collected the costume and egg. One of them gave Nancy an envelope. "That's for helping us out," he said.

9 — Inside the envelope were some tickets for the pantomime. "Oh, super!" cried Nancy. "Now we can all see the show." Nancy grinned when she saw "Mother Goose" on stage. "Our patient looks very well now," she laughed.

My dolly's wardrobe

My dolly has all kinds of clothes,
  Inside her tiny wardrobe there.
I wash them in soap bubbles, then
  Make sure they're ironed with great care.

Her pink dress is for picnics on
  The lawn with jelly, tea and cakes,
With Teddy, Lamb and Puppet Clown,
  And Ben, the Great Dane, when he wakes!

When Poodle's woollen ear was torn,
  She wore her nurse's cloak of red,
To help me wind the bandage round
  Our favourite doggy patient's head.

Smart jeans, striped shirt and cap she'll wear
  When dolls' spring-cleaning time is here.
We polish all the dolls' house floors
  And windows till they shine so clear!

I've made her lovely evening gown,
  From lacy curtain, white and fine.
It's sewed with tiny stitches for
  The pretty dolly who's all mine!

Patsy's busy day

PATSY POTTER'S daddy owned a pet shop and, every Saturday, Patsy helped out in the shop. Patsy loved to feed the puppies and kittens, the hamsters and the tropical fish.

One Saturday, Mr Potter said, "Patsy, I have to dash across to the Post Office before it closes. Can you look after the shop for a few minutes?"

"Of course," said Patsy.

Mr Potter had no sooner gone out the door, when a lady customer walked in. It was Johnnie Baker's mother.

"Hello, Patsy!" she called. "Johnnie has been ill and I've decided to buy him a pet to cheer him up. Have you any idea what I could get for him? I don't want a big animal as we live in a flat."

Patsy looked around the shop.

2 — "Perhaps Johnnie would like a fish?" suggested Patsy. "Come and look at the tank. There are lots of pretty, coloured ones — and fish are easy to look after."

"Well," sighed Mrs Baker, "they're certainly very pretty. But I think Johnnie would like a pet he could play with."

Patsy scratched her head. "A puppy or a kitten would be no use in a flat," she said.

3 — Suddenly, Patsy caught sight of the hamster cages.

"We have some lovely, golden hamsters over here," said the girl.

Mrs Baker liked the furry, little animals.

"Let me see that one," she said, pointing to a cute, wee hamster.

Carefully, Patsy picked up the hamster and placed him on the table.

"I think he'll do perfectly," said Mrs Baker. "Now I'll need to buy a cage for him."

Patsy brought over some hamster cages. "This one has plenty of room for him to run around in," explained Patsy.

4 — "I'm sure Johnnie's hamster would love that one," said Mrs Baker, as she turned round to look at the hamster. But there was a shock in store. The little furry animal had disappeared off the table!

"Oh, no!" gasped Patsy. "Where has he got to?"

"Don't worry, dear," said Mrs Baker. "I'll help you look for him. He can't have gone far. You search over beside the puppies and I'll look behind these sacks of animal food."

Patsy and Mrs Baker began to search. "I can't see him anywhere!" wailed Patsy.

5 — Just then, the doorbell rang loudly and in walked Annabel Davies, Patsy's best friend. When she saw Patsy and Mrs Baker down on their hands and knees, she began to giggle.

"You *do* look funny," she chuckled.

Quickly, Patsy told Annabel about the missing hamster.

"I'll join in the search," decided Annabel.

"Who would have thought something as small as a hamster could cause so much bother!" laughed Mrs Baker.

"Look!" cried Annabel suddenly. "I think that's him over there beside the sacks of grain."

6 — The two girls quietly crept over to the sacks. "We've got him this time," grinned Annabel.

But, just as they were about to catch the hamster, it dashed off again.

"Quickly!" shrieked Patsy. "After him."

The two girls ran after the hamster. In the end, Annabel was the one to catch the furry creature.

As quick as a flash, the girl whisked up the hamster and gave it to Patsy.

Just then, the shop door opened and in walked Mr Potter.

"Whatever is going on?" he gasped, when he saw Mrs Baker getting up off her hands and knees.

7 — "Oh, Mr Potter!" laughed Johnnie's mother, "what an enjoyable morning I've spent in your shop with Patsy. She's an excellent sales-woman."

Then Mrs Baker paid for the hamster and the new cage.

"Now *I* want a goldfish," smiled Annabel. When she'd chosen the fish, Patsy popped it into a plastic bag full of water.

"Come and have lunch at my house, Patsy," suggested Annabel.

"Oh, lovely!" grinned Patsy. "I think I deserve a rest after my busy morning!"

Tea-time puzzles

Can you tell which two cakes are exactly alike?

There are six forks hidden on these pages. Can you find them?

Try to spot six differences between these two pictures.

Join the dots to see what is shading the dolly, then lead her chum through the maze to join her.

Unscramble the letters to see what is on today's menu.

Answers:- tea, lemonade, cakes, biscuits, sandwiches, jelly.

∴ Menu ∴
aet
eonmdael
seack
isictbus
sciwdsehna
lleiy

Which of these goodies is the odd one out?

Answer:- The glass of milk, because it has to be drunk.

You can colour this picture, using your paints or crayons.

Sam

SHONA MACGREGOR has a clever sheepdog called Sam. They live on a farm in the Scottish Highlands. Shona has had Sam since he was a puppy. They are great friends and go everywhere together.

One Saturday morning, Shona's school was having an outing to the zoo. Sam was allowed to go with his chum. He *did* enjoy seeing the animals.

2 — As the zoo keeper led the children round, he told them all about the animals. Then he stopped outside the tigers' den.

"Oh, look!" cried Shona. "There's a little tiger cub. His mother is washing him."

"His name is Sultan," explained the keeper. "He was born a few days ago."

The children enjoyed seeing the rest of the animals. But everyone in Shona's class agreed that Sultan was their favourite.

Next week, when Shona was at school, her teacher, Miss McNair, told the children she wanted them to do a project about tigers.

First of all, the children drew pictures of tigers and tiger cubs.

"They're super," said Miss McNair, as she pinned them on the wall. "I *do* like your tiger cub drawing, Shona. It looks just like Sultan. I think I will write to Sultan's keeper and invite him to come along to the school and see all these lovely pictures. Perhaps he can tell us how young Sultan is getting on."

A few days later, Miss McNair had some exciting news for Shona's class.

"I have written to Sultan's keeper and he will be delighted to come and see us," said Miss McNair. "But the really exciting news is that he is going to bring Sultan with him!"

3 — Shona told Sam about Sultan's visit when she got home that day.

On the morning of the visit, Shona was up bright and early.

"I wish Sultan would come to your school every day," teased Mr MacGregor. "Then perhaps you'd always get up so early, Shona!"

As soon as Shona had eaten her breakfast, she hurried down the garden path.

"Come on, Sam!" she called. "You can come with me and see Sultan, too."

However, when they reached the school gates, Miss McNair was standing in the playground.

"I'm afraid Sam can't come to school today," the teacher told Shona. "Sultan's keeper doesn't want the little cub to get frightened."

4 — Sadly, Shona told her chum he would have to go home.

"I know you wouldn't harm Sultan, but we must do as Miss McNair says," she explained. Shona watched as her chum turned around and walked off down the road.

Meanwhile, Shona's classmates were gathering round Sultan.

"He's just like a big kitten," smiled Shona, as she stroked Sultan's fur.

"He's a little afraid," explained the zoo keeper. "This is the first time he's been out of the zoo."

Suddenly, the school bell began to ring.

5 — Poor Sultan was startled by the unexpected noise. He broke away from his keeper and ran off across the playground. Then, with a huge leap, the little tiger cub was up on the school wall. Suddenly, he jumped off the top!

"Quick!" yelled the keeper. "We must catch him before he gets too far away."

Sam, who was walking along the road, heard all the noise and raced back to the school gates. He was in time to see Sultan leaping over the wall and racing off across the road.

Sam began to bark to let Shona know he was there.

"Oh, Sam!" cried Shona, when she saw her chum. "I *am* glad to see you. Sultan has run away."

Just then, the keeper ran past Shona. "There's Sultan!" he cried, pointing to the little tiger cub. But Sultan was too fast for anyone to catch him.

6 — In no time at all, Sultan had left the keeper and the school children far behind. The tiger cub was making for the moors.

"We'll never catch him if he gets on to the moors!" gasped the keeper. "What will I do now?"

Sam began to paw at Shona's hand.

"Of course!" said Shona. "Sam can find Sultan. He knows every inch of the moors."

"Well," said Miss McNair doubtfully, "I suppose he's our only hope of finding the cub."

"Right, Sam!" said Shona. "Off you go."

Just as the sheepdog was about to dash off, he grabbed a small, red ball, which one of Shona's chums was playing with.

"Hey!" cried the girl. "Why does Sam want my ball?"

"He must have a plan to use it," said Shona.

7 — Shona was right! Sam did have a plan. The clever sheepdog raced on to the moors. In no time at all, he caught sight of the runaway cub.

Sam knew he had to be careful that he didn't frighten the cub again. So, quietly, he made his way towards the little animal.

By now, Sultan was feeling tired after his run. As he settled down beside a huge rock, Sam crept up to the rock. Then he dropped the red ball and watched as it bounced over to Sultan.

When the little animal saw the bouncing ball, he thought it was a game. He pounced on the ball and began to pat it.

While Sultan was busy playing with the ball, Sam grabbed hold of the cub by his collar. Then, the sheepdog began to lead the tiger cub back to the school.

8 — Every few minutes, Sam gave the little cub a help by carrying him. When they were near the school, Shona caught sight of them.

"There's Sam!" she cried. "And he's got Sultan with him!"

The keeper ran over to help Sam.

"Well done!" he said gratefully. "I don't know how to thank you enough. Shona was right when she said you were the one to bring Sultan back."

The keeper put the lead back on the cub.

"You *are* a rascal, Sultan," he laughed.

Sultan began to prance about in front of Sam.

"He wants to play with his new friend," said Miss McNair. "It's just as well Sam came along with you today, Shona. He's been a great help."

Jolly Jollykins

"I'M sorry, Emma," said Mummy, "but you won't be able to go to the circus after all. The doctor says you have measles and must stay in the house for a few days."

Poor Emma was very sad. She had been looking forward to the circus for such a long time.

Emma stared out of the window. It had been raining and now a rainbow appeared right above her garden shed. Just then, she saw the shed door swing open.

"It must be the wind," thought Emma. As she watched the door swing open, a strange little creature came out of the shed. It had a fluffy body, big, brown eyes and a turned up nose. But the strangest sight of all were its little *blue ears*!

Emma was amazed when the creature opened the window and climbed right into the room beside her.

"*Who are you*?" the little girl gasped.

"My name is Jollykins," replied the friendly creature. "I've come to cheer you up! But, first of all, let's jolly up this room."

Jollykins wiggled her ears and, suddenly, the room was filled with all the colours of the rainbow.

"It's *beautiful*!" gasped Emma. "But what can you do to cheer *me* up?"

"That's easy!" laughed Jollykins. "I'll magic some playmates for you."

She wiggled her ears again and, in an instant, the room was full of jolly, playful kittens. Emma had super fun playing with them. They darted here and there and leapt about doing all sorts of acrobatic tricks.

"It's just like my own private circus!" cried Emma.

Jollykins smiled and wiggled her ears again.

"And now," said Jollykins, "open the door, Emma, because a friend of yours is outside and wants to visit you."

Emma opened the door and her teddy walked in!

"Winnie!" gasped Emma. "This *is* a surprise. I didn't know you could walk!"

"I can talk, too," laughed Winnie. Emma gave her teddy a great, big hug.

"Let's play hide-and-seek," suggested Winnie.

Winnie and Emma played for a long time.

"Are you enjoying yourself?" Jollykins asked Emma.

"Ooh, yes!" cried the little girl.

"Good," said Jollykins with a smile. "I have one more surprise for you. Close your eyes!"

"You can look now," said Jollykins.

Emma clapped her hands with joy when she saw *all* her toys had come alive.

"And now for some more jolly fun," announced Jollykins.

The toys did somersaults and cartwheels,while the kittens jumped over brightly coloured balloons!

"I can do cartwheels, too!" cried Emma. "Just watch."

Jollykins laughed, "Well, you certainly look happy. I must go and cheer up someone else now. Good-bye, Emma."

As Emma waved good-bye to her friend, she suddenly felt very sleepy. When she woke up, the kittens were gone and her toys were just toys once again.

"What a super afternoon I had," thought Emma with a smile. "It was as good as a trip to the circus!"

Plain Jane and the Princess

Princess Jane was just as a princess should be. She had lovely, long golden hair, and a pretty face with big, blue eyes.

Jane lived happily in a huge palace with her mother and father, the king and the queen, and she had everything she could possibly want. She wore beautiful clothes and jewels, and played with lovely toys and dolls.

Princess Jane enjoyed being a princess and, when she went out, people would stop to bow or curtsey.

2 — In the village, near the royal palace, there lived another little girl, also called Jane. But this little girl wasn't in the least bit like a princess. She was very ordinary and had short, straight, brown hair and brown eyes.

Everybody called this Jane, Plain Jane, and she lived with her mummy and daddy in a small cottage. Jane helped her mother in the house and did the shopping for her, too. Then she would help her father in the garden. They were poor and grew all their own vegetables.

This Jane didn't have fancy clothes or a lot of toys, but she was happy just the same.

3 — One day, when Princess Jane was in the town, she met Plain Jane. The little girl tried to curtsey, but she did it very badly and Princess Jane laughed. She had never seen such a plain girl before and she was amazed.

Plain Jane had never seen a beautiful princess before. *She* was amazed, too.

After a few minutes, the two girls began chatting, and they found that they got on well together.

One day, Princess Jane and Plain Jane thought up a plan. They decided that it would be rather fun to change places for a while.

4 — The two girls changed into each other's clothes and put on wigs.

"You look almost like a princess already!" cried the princess. She fastened a pearl necklace around Plain Jane's neck and gave her a pair of silver shoes to wear.

5 — So, later, the new Princess Jane went off to the palace, while the new Plain Jane went to the cottage.

That night, Princess Jane had her supper at a big table, spread with all sorts of different meats, puddings and cream cakes. She had never tasted such rich food before, and didn't really like it.

As Jane lay in her big bed that night, she felt quite hungry and, not being used to such a soft mattress, she found she couldn't sleep.

6 — Meanwhile, the real princess had sat down to have Plain Jane's supper in the cottage. In front of her was a big piece of bread, some hard cheese and dry biscuits. She wasn't used to food like that, and couldn't eat it, so *she* went to bed feeling very hungry, too.

Then *she* couldn't sleep in Plain Jane's small, hard bed.

Next morning, the princess was sent off to do the shopping. It was a long walk to the market and she felt cold in her thin dress. The streets were crowded and she had to push her way among all the people.

7 — After that, the new Plain Jane realised that she'd had enough of being ordinary.

Meanwhile, Plain Jane had decided she didn't want to be a princess any longer. So both Janes set off back to their real homes, and met each other on the way. They sat down and laughed until the tears ran down their cheeks.

"Goodbye, Jane!" called the real princess, later. "I'm going home for some proper food — roast chicken and chocolate cake."

"Good-bye, Jane!" said the real Plain Jane. "I'm going home for some proper food, too — bread and cheese."

And, to this day, the two girls have stayed the best of friends.

Dotty Doodles

She's quick on the draw with felt-tip pens.

1 — Hello, girls. I'm drawing a girl. She's called Polly.

2 — She *is* sweet. Now I've drawn her a car.

3 — Polly loves driving. Look out, Polly!

4 — Oh, dear! Now she's crashed the car into a tree.

5 — The car's damaged. Never mind, I'll help.

6 — I'll draw another car for Polly.

7 — There! It's finished. I hope Polly likes it.

8 — Ho! Ho! It won't matter if Polly bumps this *dodgem* car!

1 — There was only one day left until Jenny's birthday. She and her friends were going to see a pantomime. Jenny was so excited she could hardly sleep that night.

2 — In the morning, Jenny got up early and looked through the window. "It's snowing!" she gasped. "Snow *and* a pantomime on my birthday. I *am* lucky!"

3 — But Jenny's mummy had bad news for her. "The snow has blocked the road into town," she said. "We won't be able to go to the pantomime after all."

4 — Jenny *was* disappointed. "I *hate* the snow!" she grumbled. Jenny went into her bedroom to play. She didn't notice Mummy making lots of phone calls.

5 — That afternoon, Jenny heard voices outside. She looked out of the window and saw all her friends coming up the garden path! They were pulling their sledges.

6 — "Your mummy decided to have a party for you," they explained. "She phoned and invited us this morning." "What a lovely surprise," said Jenny with a smile.

7 — "Let's play some party games," said Mummy. "Ooh, yes!" they all cried. "Can we play 'musical chairs'?" asked Jenny. "That's a good idea," said Mummy.

8 — Jenny and her chums played party games until everyone had won a prize. Then Mummy called, "Time for tea!" "Hurray!" the children cheered.

9 — There were lots of lovely things to eat. But best of all was the birthday cake! "I'll blow out the candles and make a wish!" exclaimed Jenny. "Here goes."

10 — Moments later, Mummy called, "I've just heard that the road is clear. We can go to the pantomime." "My birthday wish has come true!" cried Jenny.

Silver Lady

MARY MARTIN loved her rocking horse. Every night, before bed, she would climb on Dobbin's back and pretend they were taking part in a show jumping competition. And, if she half closed her eyes, she could imagine the daisies on her wall-paper were ladies' hats.

"Ten minutes till bed-time," Mummy said, one night.

"Oh, good!" thought Mary. She rocked faster and faster. Suddenly, the daisies on the wall seemed to move, and then Mary heard cheering and clapping . . .

. . . Mary looked down at the floor, but, instead of carpet, she saw grass! And Dobbin was now a *real* horse!

Mary heard her name being called over a loudspeaker.

"Ladies and gentlemen, Mary Martin on Silver Lady. They only need a clear round to win," the announcer said.

"Come on, Silver Lady," whispered Mary. "We can do it."

Mary and Silver Lady set off. They sailed over the gates and fences.

"Now the wall," thought Mary. Silver Lady's hoof caught a brick. The crowd gasped. But the brick didn't fall.

There was only the water jump to cross. Everyone held their breath as Mary and Silver Lady soared across.

"We've done it!" cried Mary. She was given a beautiful silver cup and a red rosette.

"Well done," said the lady who was presenting the prizes.

Suddenly, Mary felt very sleepy and heard Mummy's voice.

"You can't sleep on Dobbin," Mummy laughed.

"She isn't Dobbin any more," Mary yawned. "She's a champion show jumper called Silver Lady!"

The fancy dress party

TWINKLE came home from school, one day, just before Christmas. She had some exciting news to tell Mummy. There was to be a very special party for her class.

"Teacher says we can take our favourite toys to the party!" cried Twinkle. "And they're to be wearing fancy dress."

"Which toy will you take?" asked Mummy.

2 — Twinkle couldn't decide which toy would go to the party with her. She went up to her room and got out her dollies.

"I *have* a lot of dollies," sighed Twinkle, "but I can't take them *all* to the party. What will I do?"

Then she noticed her teddy sitting alone in a corner.

"I know!" cried Twinkle. "I'll take Teddy! We could make him a lovely outfit!"

She hurried downstairs.

3 — That evening, Twinkle and Mummy sat down to make a costume for Teddy.

"What would you like him to have?" asked Mummy.

"Could you make a clown's costume?" asked Twinkle.

Mummy fetched her bag of scraps and made Teddy a cute pair of baggy trousers.

Next, she sewed up a bright, red waistcoat, and tied a spotted bow tie round Teddy's neck. Last of all, Twinkle put one of her dollies' hats on his head.

"There!" she said. "Doesn't he look sweet!"

4 — On the afternoon of the party, Twinkle and her mummy left the house early. They had to collect Twinkle's friend, Tracy.

When she reached Tracy's house, Twinkle knocked at the door.
"I'm taking my doll, Rose," explained Tracy, as she came out. Rose was dressed as the Queen of Hearts and she wore a gold crown.
"Mummy even made her a plate of jam tarts," Tracy went on.

At last, the excited little girls hurried off to the party. All the other children had brought a toy in fancy dress and there was lots to eat and lots of games to play.

5 — "Did you have a good time?" Twinkle's mummy asked when she came to collect Twinkle and Tracy. "And did Teddy and Rose win a prize?"
"We *all* got a prize!" cried Twinkle. "Oh, Mummy! I've left Teddy in the party room!"

"And Rose is there, too!" added Tracy.
They hurried off to collect their toys.
The girls found Teddy and Rose sitting in a corner of the room together. They *did* look funny.

"Look!" whispered Tracy. "They seem to be asleep. And the plate the jam tarts were on is *empty*!"
"Then I think our toys have enjoyed the party as much as we did!" laughed Twinkle.

Pet show puzzles

You can colour this picture, using your paints or crayons.

Try to spot six differences between these two pictures.

Unscramble the names on these dog tags.
Answers:-

PRINCE, FIDO, REX, HONEY.

Can you tell which two mice are exactly alike?

There are six collars hidden on this page. Can you find them?

Belinda's flying brolly

1 — Belinda and her mummy were out shopping when, suddenly, it started to rain. "I'll buy you a rain-hat," said Mummy. "I don't like hats," groaned Belinda.

2 — "Can I have an umbrella instead?" pleaded Belinda. "I already have a rain-hat at home." Mummy agreed and she bought Belinda a beautiful, red umbrella.

3 — Belinda loved her umbrella. She skipped along the pavement, holding it up proudly. "I like the sound the rain makes on my brolly," she said to Mummy.

4 — When they reached the supermarket, Belinda asked, "Can I stay outside?" "All right," replied Mummy. "But don't wander off." The wind tugged at Belinda's brolly.

5 — Suddenly — whoosh! The wind lifted Belinda and her umbrella right up into the air. "Oooh, help!" cried Belinda. She held on tightly to the umbrella handle.

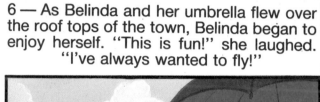

6 — As Belinda and her umbrella flew over the roof tops of the town, Belinda began to enjoy herself. "This is fun!" she laughed. "I've always wanted to fly!"

7 — Then Belinda noticed there were other people in the sky as well as her, all holding umbrellas. "It's like a fairground," she gasped. "Good day!" everyone called out.

8 — Belinda wanted to stay with her new friends longer, but the wind carried her towards the sea-side. "Hello!" she cried to a passing seagull. He *did* get a surprise!

9 — The wind changed direction and Belinda found herself in the "fairground" again. "Have a toffee apple, dear!" a lady said. "Thank you," Belinda replied.

10 — The umbrella took Belinda back to town. She landed on the pavement in front of the supermarket, just as Mummy came out. "Look what I've got!" Belinda cried.

11 — "Goodness!" gasped Belinda's mummy. "Where did you get that from?" "Someone gave it to me when I was flying in the sky," said Belinda.

12 — On the way home, Belinda told Mummy all about the "fairground" in the sky and the toffee apple lady. "I bought you a *magic* brolly!" Mummy laughed.

Benny

MY brother's name is Benny, and
He's nearly three years old.
When Benny's fast asleep in bed,
He looks as good as gold.

But, oh dear! What a difference
When he is wide awake.
He bumps and thumps and jumps until
The floor begins to shake.

He goes up high upon the swing,
Then shouts, " Look, I'm in space!"
He'll never be an astronaut
With such a dirty face!

On quiet days, Ben makes a noise
With his big, fancy drum.
" I'm keeping you awake," he laughs.
" No *chance* of sleep!" says Mum.

Sometimes he climbs the apple tree
And then he can't get down.
He puts Mum's make-up on his face,
And says that he's a clown.

He loves all creepy, crawly things,
Like worms and snails and slugs.
And if he doesn't know their names,
He calls them " wriggly-bugs "!

Sometimes he is so mischievous
That even Gran's amazed.
She shakes her head and says to Mum,
" That boy leaves me quite dazed!"

We're glad when Benny goes to bed,
Because it's nice and calm.
And when he's sleeping, Benny looks
A proper little lamb!

Play the Twinkle game

Start

To play this game, all you need is a dice and the counters on the right. Cut these out, paste them on to cardboard and give one to each player. Throw a six to start, then, next throw, off you go!

The first player to reach Twinkle is the winner.

1

2

3

4
You help Nurse Nancy repair some dollies. Go on 4 places.

5

6

7

Patch is lost, so you take him home. Go back 5 places.

8

9

10
Miss a turn while you watch the Blobs' cycle Race.

11

12

HELP

ME!

13
Rescue Elfie from a toy yacht. Go forward 4 places.

14

15

16

Fiona's fairy friend

LEILA was a tiny fairy who lived in a secret wood. She loved to go exploring.

One day, she came upon a branch lying across a brook. Tip-toeing along it, Leila leaned over to look into the water. Snap! A twig broke and Leila fell in with a *splash*!

"Help!" cried Leila as she was swept along.

2 — Soon, the wood was left far behind. Leila held on tightly to the twig. All of a sudden, it bumped into the bank and Leila scrambled on to the grass.

She pushed her way through the grass until she saw what seemed to her a huge stone building.

"That must be a house," thought Leila.

3 — Leila crept closer. There were flowers and a road leading up to the big front door.

The fairy went closer and saw a smaller door which swung open. Leila pushed it and climbed inside.

"Eek!" she screamed. Leila had never seen a dog before. She took to her heels and ran!

4 — "A fairy! A *real* fairy!" cried a voice, suddenly. It came from a girl called Fiona.
She scooped Leila up in her hand. Shyly, Leila told Fiona all about her adventures.

"And now I miss my home," she sighed. "I wish I hadn't wandered off at all."
"Well you must stay here for the night," said Fiona. "You'd never find your way back in the dark."

5 — After a while, Fiona and the fairy both began to feel tired. "Fairies have to sleep, too," yawned Leila.
"Then you can stay in my dolls' house!" cried Fiona. Very carefully, she carried the fairy over to the dolls' house, tucked her up and went to bed.

Next morning, Fiona jumped out of bed and ran over to the dolls' house. She *was* disappointed when she found her fairy friend had gone!

6 — Fiona looked all over her bedroom, but Leila was nowhere to be seen. Fiona's mummy came in and found Fiona sitting on the floor looking very sad.

Fiona told her all about the fairy.
"I've looked everywhere and she's not here," sobbed the little girl.
"Don't worry," said Mummy. "I think you must have had a lovely dream."

Some weeks later, Fiona was settling down to sleep when she heard a tapping on the window. "Let me in!" a tiny voice called.

7 — It was Leila. "So you *are* real!" gasped Fiona.
"I came to thank you for helping me," said Leila. "I can grant you one wish for being so kind."

8 — "I wish for a fairy doll who looks just like you," said Fiona. "I'll see what I can do," called the tiny fairy before she flew away.

9 — Next day, Fiona opened up her dolls' house. There, she saw a beautiful doll on the bed. And, guess what! She looked just like Leila.

ELFIE

Elfie is a tiny elf who lives secretly in Mary's doll's house. When he makes things happen, Mary thinks it is magic. Poochie, Mary's big dog, is Elfie's best friend.

1 — One morning, Elfie got a party invitation from the mice who lived under the garden shed. "Oh, super!" cried Elfie, happily. "I love going to Christmas parties."

2 — Then Elfie thought, "I must wrap up my Christmas presents." But he didn't have any wrapping paper. Elfie went into the room where Mary was wrapping up her presents. "I'll use Mary's left-over paper," he decided.

3 — When Mary went away for lunch, Elfie quickly picked up the paper and ribbons Mary didn't want. "I have more than enough now!" he said with a smile.

4 — Later, Elfie put on his warm clothes and made his way down to the garden shed. "Oh, no!" he wailed. "The snow is much too deep for me to walk through."

5 — Elfie went sadly back home. "I *was* looking forward to the party," he sighed. Suddenly, the little elf saw one of Mary's Christmas cards and had an idea.

6 — "I could *ski* to the party!" Elfie cried. "Why didn't I think of that before!" He rushed to the toy cupboard and borrowed a doll's skis. "Mary won't mind," he said.

7 — The little elf put on his cosy skiing outfit and packed his presents for the mice in a sack. "I feel like Father Christmas with all these gifts!" he giggled.

8 — Elfie set off through the deep snow. "Hooray!" cried the mouse family when they saw him. "We were afraid the snow would stop you coming to the party."

9 — Elfie gave the mice their presents and then they all sat down to tea. "This is a *super* party!" said Elfie. "Merry Christmas!" "Merry Christmas!" cried the mice.

Dainty Decorations

To make these jolly snowmen, fold a strip of thin paper like this and draw a snowman on the top. Cut around the snowman shape, unfold the paper, then colour your snowman with paints or crayons.

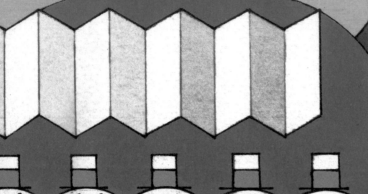

Here's how to make brightly-coloured paper chains.

Cut off a short strip of gummed, coloured paper and stick the ends together to make a loop. Continue by threading on new different-coloured loops until the chain is the length you want.

Paper doyleys make a table look very pretty. Take a square of paper and fold it three times as shown. Then cut out a shape from each side, open it up carefully and hey presto — a beautiful doyley!

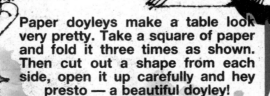

Festive table mats are very useful! Fold over a square piece of card and make cuts with scissors where the lines are shown. Next, cut strips of coloured paper, the length of your mat, and weave them into the square to make any pattern you like.

Now make your very own Christmas fairy. Twist three pipe cleaners together like this. Make the head by packing a square of material with cotton wool and gathering it at the neck. Tie firmly on to the pipe cleaner. Sew hair on as shown.

No Christmas is complete without Santa! Make a cone of red paper for the body, then use paper or material to add a funny face and clothing as shown.

The fairy's dress is easy to make. Sew a strip of material into a tube shape, then turn it right side out and gather tightly round the neck.
Finish the fairy by cutting wings out of card and sewing them on to the dress.

Molly and her Dollies

Molly is a little girl whose toys all came to life. You see, Molly made a wish when she saw a shooting star — and her wish came true! Now her toys walk and talk!

1 — It was a few days before Christmas and Molly and the toys were decorating their tree. "It looks super," said Molly. "I think I'll put my presents under it," decided Teddy.

2 — Then they noticed the birds outside. "I wish *they* had a Christmas tree, too," sighed Julie. "They look unhappy sitting on those bare branches." Suddenly, Molly had an idea.

3 — Molly told the toys to fetch bits of bread and bacon and apples. Teddy even found half a coconut! "We'll tie ribbon on them," said Molly. The toys *were* puzzled.

4 — Later, Molly and the toys put on their coats and hats and went outside into the garden. They decorated the tree with the food. "I hope the birds like it," said Tina.

5 — Molly and the toys stood quietly and watched the birds as they tucked into their special feast. A blackbird chirped cheerily. "I think they *do* like their Christmas tree!" laughed Tina.

Bubbles the washday witch

1 — Sally was washing her dolls' clothes in a bowl of soapy water. Mummy was doing her washing, too, in the washing-machine.

All the clothes were whirling round and round among the bubbles. Suddenly, the machine stopped and Mummy couldn't get it to start again!

"Oh, dear!" sighed Mummy. "Now it will take ages to do the washing." Sally *was* disappointed. Mummy had promised to take her to the park, later.

Then Mummy had to go and answer the front door.

"I wish the washing machine hadn't broken down!" sighed Sally.

"What was that?" asked a voice.

Sally saw a strange, little old lady.

"Who are *you*?" asked Sally.

"I'm Bubbles," said the old lady. "Bubbles, the washday witch."

2 — "Don't worry, I won't hurt you. I go into people's houses and help out when things go wrong on washing day."

"What sort of things?" asked Sally.

"I mend clothes lines that snap. I make the soap powder bubble up when it should," said Bubbles. "All you have to do is make a wish. Try it for yourself."

3 — "I wish my dolls' clothes were out to dry," said Sally.

"That's easy!" cried Bubbles, and she chanted a little magic rhyme.

4 — "Look out of the window," Bubbles said. There, fluttering in the breeze, were the dolls' clothes.

"Now I'll fix your mummy's machine," said Bubbles.

Then the door opened and Mummy came in.

"The machine's working!" cried Sally, taking her hand.

5 — Mummy went over and looked in. The clothes were whirling busily round and round in the soapy water.

"Mummy, I want you to come and meet Bubbles," said Sally, turning round to look for the kind, old lady. But she had vanished!

"What did you say, dear?" called Mummy.

"Oh, er, nothing," murmured Sally.

In no time at all, the washing was done, so Sally helped Mummy hang it on the line and then they set off for the park.

Sally was glad that she and Mummy could get out for the afternoon, and it was all thanks to Bubbles, the washday witch!

Christmas puzzle time

You can colour this picture of Little Jack Horner with your paints or crayons.

Unscramble the jumbled letters to find out what this song is.

YOLLH and the YVI

Which two of these "three ships a-sailing in" are exactly alike?

Lead the carol singer through the maze to join his friends singing "Good King Wenceslas".

Don't forget! "Twinkle", the picture paper specially for little girls, is on sale every Wednesday.

Patch

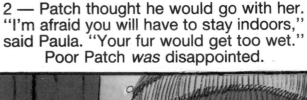

1 — Paula Perkins has a cute, little kitten called Patch. He likes to join in with everything Paula does. It was snowing and Paula decided to go out and play.

2 — Patch thought he would go with her. "I'm afraid you will have to stay indoors," said Paula. "Your fur would get too wet." Poor Patch *was* disappointed.

3 — "Now, if only we had an igloo," sighed Paula, "we could play at eskimos." Just then, Patch saw Daddy take his golfing umbrella out into the garden.

4 — Before Paula went out, she showed Patch a picture she'd found of some eskimos with their igloo. Patch wished *he* had an igloo. It certainly looked cosy.

5 — But Paula's daddy had an idea. He had taken his golfing umbrella and put it up in the garden. Later, Paula noticed Patch was missing. "I know where he is," smiled Daddy. "Come with me and I'll show you, Paula."

6 — How Paula laughed when she saw her cheeky, little kitten sitting under Dad's umbrella. "He's nice and dry in his own little 'igloo'," giggled Paula.

The BLOBS

. . . bright little Blobs of paint who burst out of a paintbox into the wonderful world of Paintbox Land.

FIZZY ORANGE had invited eight Blob friends to his house for a Christmas party.

After tea, there were fun and games. The Blobs *did* enjoy themselves! Even Grumbly Green didn't grumble at all.

Fizzy had hung eight presents on the Christmas tree — one for each of his chums. All the gifts were books and each Blob had to find his own one. (That gave Grumbly something to grumble about!)

Can you guess which book each Blob took home?

Here are the books which each of the Blobs took home:—

Ghostly White took the book about HAUNTED CASTLES, of course.

The "SPELLING" FOR WITCHES book was for Inky Black.

King Royal Blue went home with the book about SCOTTISH CASTLES.

Grumbly Green took HOW TO COMPLAIN IN 6 LANGUAGES.

The CHEESES OF THE WORLD book was for Mousey Brown.

Sailor Blue took the book about SAILING BOATS.

Primrose Yellow chose the FLOWERS FOR SPRING book.

The POP MUSIC book was taken by Poppy Red.

Now in Fairyland you see
All the merry company.
Our small friends, they're one and all
At the Fairy Queen's Grand Ball.

There, beneath the moon so bright,
They will sing and dance all night.
While wee children, sleepy heads,
Curl up in their cosy beds.